W9-BRB-587

SAINTS
A BOOK OF DAYS

Saint Francis and the Bishop of Assisi Admit Saint Clare to the Franciscan Order

SAINTS
A BOOK OF DAYS

The Metropolitan Museum of Art

A Bulfinch Press Book
Little, Brown and Company

BOSTON · NEW YORK · LONDON · TORONTO

All works of art reproduced in this book are from the collections of
The Metropolitan Museum of Art, New York.

Copyright © 1994 by The Metropolitan Museum of Art
All rights reserved.

First Edition

ISBN 0-87099-716-5 (MMA)
ISBN 0-8212-2173-6 (Bulfinch Press)

Published by
The Metropolitan Museum of Art and Bulfinch Press
Bulfinch Press is an imprint and trademark of Little, Brown and Company (Inc.)
Published simultaneously in Canada by
Little, Brown & Company (Canada) Limited

Produced by the Department of Special Publications,
The Metropolitan Museum of Art
Designed by Tina Fjotland

Printed in Italy
Second printing

The saints are the heroes of the Church: men and women who distinguished themselves by their virtue, wisdom, courage, or devotion, whose stories are meant to inspire and instruct. The lives and legends of the saints—their likenesses, miracles, and martyrdoms—have been a favorite subject of storytellers and artists since earliest Christian times and form one of the richest veins of imagery in the Western cultural tradition.

The images of the saints and of the Holy Family included in this book have been chosen from the collections of The Metropolitan Museum of Art. Of the thousands of possible examples available there, in all media and dating from as early as the fourth century, we have limited our selection to European panel paintings and illuminated manuscripts of the Middle Ages and the Renaissance.

So great are the numbers of saints that their feasts more than fill the calendar. While some modern saints have been inserted, this calendar does not represent a modern cycle of feasts. Frequently it includes saints traditionally venerated in the Middle Ages and the feast days assigned to them at that time. The saints chosen for this book include many whose names are currently in use, others associated with particular countries or cities, and many whose legends have special anecdotal appeal. Any number of well-known or popular saints have unfortunately been omitted due to limitations of space. A brief description has been added for each saint, with an indication for many of them of special devotions linked to their names.

Barbara Drake Boehm
Associate Curator, Medieval Art

Laurence B. Kanter
Curator in Charge, Robert Lehman Collection

The Presentation of Christ in the Temple (January 1)
Detail from a panel
Giovanni di Paolo, Italian (Sienese), born ca. 1400, d. 1482
Tempera and gold on panel
Gift of George Blumenthal, 1941   41.100.4

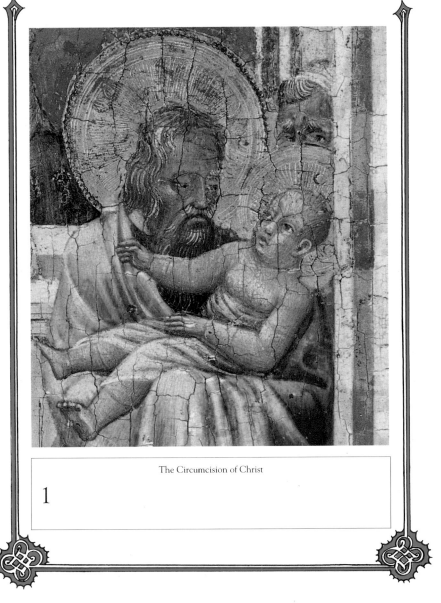

The Circumcision of Christ

1

Adoration of the Magi (January 6)
Master of James IV of Scotland, Netherlandish (Bruges)
Tempera on parchment, ca. 1515
Bequest of George D. Pratt, 1935   48.149.15

JANUARY

Macarius of Alexandria (301–391), desert monk, patron of pastry chefs

2

Genevieve (ca. 422–500), patron of Paris

3

Elizabeth Seton (1774–1821), first North–American-born saint

4

Simeon Stylites (ca. 390–459), pillar ascetic

5

The Epiphany

6

Tillo, abbot of Solignac (d. ca. 702)

7

Lucian, bishop of Beauvais (d. ca. 290)

8

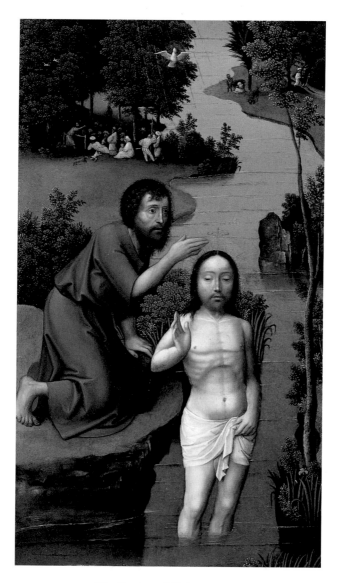

The Baptism of Christ (January 13)
Detail from the left panel of a triptych, *The Penitence of Saint Jerome*
Joachim Patinir, Netherlandish, active by 1515, d. 1524
Oil on panel
Fletcher Fund, 1936   36.14b

JANUARY

Adrian, abbot of St. Augustine's, Canterbury (d. 709/10)

9

William, archbishop of Bourges (d. 1209)

10

Hyginus, pope (r. 136–140)

11

Arcadius, martyr (d. 312)

12

The Baptism of Christ

13

Hilary, bishop of Poitiers (320–368), invoked for protection from serpents

14

Paul the Hermit (229–342), patron of basket weavers

15

Saint Anthony the Abbot Tempted by a Heap of Gold (January 17)
The Osservanza Master, Italian (Sienese), active second quarter of the 15th century
Tempera and gold on panel
Robert Lehman Collection, 1975   1975.1.27

JANUARY

Fursey (d. 650), Irish abbot and missionary

16

Anthony Abbot (251–356), desert father,
patriarch of monks, invoked against skin diseases

17

Peter's Chair at Rome

18

Canute, king of the Danes (r. 1080–1086)

19

Fabian, pope (r. 236–250), patron of pewterers, and
Sebastian, third-century martyr, patron of archers,
invoked for protection against the plague

20

Agnes (d. ca. 305), patron of maidens

21

Vincent of Saragossa (d. 304), patron of winemakers, patron of sailors

22

Saint Charlemagne (January 28)
From the *Belles Heures of Jean, duke of Berry*, fol. 174r
The Limbourg Brothers, France (Paris), active ca. 1400–1416
Tempera and gold on vellum
The Cloisters Collection, 1954   54.1.1

JANUARY

23

Raymond of Peñafort (b. 1175), Dominican canonist

24

Timothy (d. 97), companion of Saint Paul and first bishop of Ephesus, invoked against upset stomach

25

Conversion of Saint Paul of Tarsus (ca. 3–ca. 64)

26

Margaret, princess of Hungary (1242–1270), Dominican nun

27

John Chrysostom, bishop of Constantinople (ca. 347–407), Doctor of the Church, patron of preachers

28

Charlemagne, Holy Roman Emperor (742–818), patron of universities

29

Francis de Sales, bishop of Geneva (1567–1622), patron of authors

The Purification of the Virgin in an Initial S (February 2)
Italian (Ferrarese), Circle of Cosimo Tura (active by 1451, d. 1495)
Tempera and gold on parchment
Rogers Fund, 1911   11.50.4

Martina of Rome, virgin martyr (d. 230)

30

John Bosco (1815–1888), founder of the Salesian order,
patron of boys, patron of editors

31

Brigid of Ireland (ca. 452–524), patron of milkmaids

1

The Purification of the Virgin (Candlemas)

2

Blaise, bishop of Sebaste, Armenia (d. 316), invoked against sore throats

3

Andrew Corsini, bishop of Fiesole (1302–1373)

4

Agatha (d. 251), patron of nursing mothers

5

Saint Dorothy (February 6)
Netherlandish or North German, ca. 1500
Tempera and gold on parchment
The Friedsam Collection
Bequest of Michael Friedsam, 1931   32.100.475c

FEBRUARY

Dorothy (d. 304), patron of florists

6

Romuald (952–1027), founder of the Camaldolese order

7

Stephen of Muret (1048–1124), founder of the Abbey of Grandmont

8

Apollonia (d. 249), patron of dentists, patron of children cutting teeth

9

Scholastica (ca. 480–547), twin sister of Saint Benedict

10

Paschal I, pope (r. 817–824)

11

Julian the Hospitaller, patron of fishmongers,
patron of travelers, patron of boatmen

12

Saint Theodulus (February 17)
Exterior wing from *The Burg Weiler Altar*
Master of the Burg Weiler Altar, German (Middle Rhenish), active ca. 1470
Tempera and oil on panel
The Cloisters Collection, 1953   53.21

FEBRUARY

Catherine dei Ricci (1523–1590), Florentine Dominican and visionary

13

Valentine (d. 273), patron of lovers

14

Sigfrid (d. ca. 1045), patron of Sweden

15

Juliana (d. 304), invoked by pregnant women

16

Theodulus, ninth-century bishop of Sion, patron of bell makers

17

Simeon (d. ca. 107), patriarch of Jerusalem, first cousin of Jesus

18

Conrad of Piacenza (1290–1351), Franciscan, invoked for the cure of hernias

19

Saint Matthias (February 24)
Detail from *Saints Matthias and Thomas*
Bartolomeo Bulgarini (Ugolino Lorenzetti), Italian (Sienese), active 1337–1378
Tempera and gold on panel
Robert Lehman Collection, 1975   1975.1.8

FEBRUARY

20
Eleutherius, bishop of Tournai (456–531)

21
Peter Damian, bishop of Ostia (1007–1072), invoked against migraines

22
Margaret of Cortona (1247–1297), patron of penitent girls

23
Polycarp, bishop of Smyrna (ca. 69–ca. 155), invoked against earaches

24
Matthias, Apostle, chosen to replace Judas

25
Victorinus, martyr (d. ca. 283)

26
Porphyry, bishop of Gaza (353–420)

The Glorification of Saint Thomas Aquinas (March 7)
Detail from a panel
Master of the Dominican Effigies, Italian (Florentine),
active second quarter of the 14th century
Tempera and gold on panel
Robert Lehman Collection, 1975   1975.1.99

Leander, bishop of Seville (ca. 550–601), invoked against rheumatism

27

Oswald, archbishop of York (d. 992)

28/29

David (d. ca. 601), patron of Wales, patron of newborns

1

Chad, bishop of York (d. 672)

2

Cunegund, empress of Germany (d 1040)

3

Casimir, prince of Poland (1458–1484)

4

Adrian of May (d. 875), Irish missionary to Scotland

5

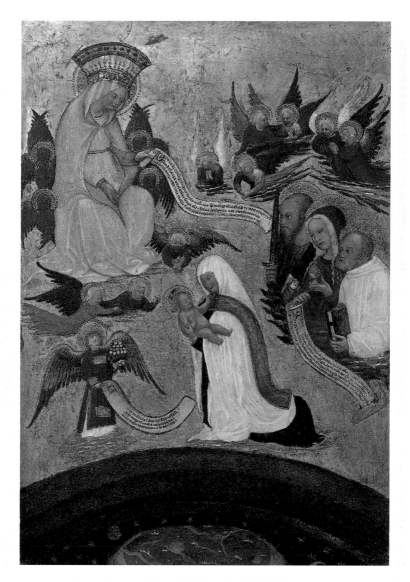

Saint Frances of Rome Holding the Christ Child (March 9)
Antonio da Viterbo the Elder (?), Italian (Roman), active ca. 1450
Tempera and gold on panel
Robert Lehman Collection, 1975   1975.1.101

MARCH

Perpetua, martyred with her slave Felicity (d. 203), patron of new mothers

6

Thomas Aquinas (ca. 1225–1274), Dominican theologian, Doctor of the Church

7

John of God (1495–1550), patron of booksellers,
patron of printers, patron of the sick

8

Frances of Rome, abbess (1394–1440), patron of widows

9

Anastasia Patricia, sixth-century virgin hermit,
pursued by Emperor Justinian

10

Sophronius, patriarch of Jerusalem (ca. 560–638)

11

Gregory the Great, pope (540–604), Doctor of the Church, patron of singers

12

Saint Joseph Leads the Virgin and Child on the Flight into Egypt (March 19)
From *The Hours of Jeanne d'Evreux*, fol. 83
Jean Pucelle, French (Paris), active ca. 1320–1350
Tempera and gold on parchment
The Cloisters Collection, 1954   54.1.2

MARCH

Nicephorus, patriarch of Constantinople (ca. 758–829)

13

Matilda of Quedlinburg (897–968), mother of Holy Roman Emperor Otto I

14

Zachary, pope (r. 741–752)

15

Heribert, archbishop of Cologne (970–1021)

16

Patrick (ca. 389–ca. 461), patron of Ireland

17

Edward the Martyr, king of England (ca. 963–978)

18

Joseph, husband of the Virgin Mary, patron of husbands

19

The Archangel Gabriel (March 24)
Detail from *The Annunciation*
Sandro Botticelli, Italian (Florentine), 1445–1510
Tempera on panel
Robert Lehman Collection, 1975   1975.1.74

MARCH

Cuthbert, bishop of Lindisfarne (d. 687)

20

Benedict (ca. 480–550), Patriarch of Western Monasticism

21

Deogratias, fifth-century bishop of Carthage

22

Turibius, archbishop of Lima (1538–1606), patron of native rights

23

The Archangel Gabriel, patron of messengers, patron of broadcasters

24

The Annunciation

25

Felix, bishop of Trier (d. ca. 400)

26

Dominica prima in aduentu dni
Sequentia sci euāgelij: s. mackei.

N illo tempore: Cum
appropinquasset iliesus
iherosolimis: et uenisset
bethphage ad montem

Christ's Entry into Jerusalem (Palm Sunday)
Southern Netherlands (?), Bruges (?), ca. 1480–90
Tempera on parchment
Robert Lehman Collection, 1975   1975.1.2471

MARCH-APRIL

John of Damascus (ca. 675–ca. 749), Doctor of the Church

27

John of Capistrano (1386–1456), patron of jurists

28

Cyril, fourth-century deacon of Heliopolis

29

Regulus, first bishop of Senlis (d. ca. 250)

30

Benjamin, fifth-century deacon of the church of Persia

31

Hugh, bishop of Grenoble (1053–1132)

1

Francis of Paola (1416–1507), invoked to protect the birth of children

2

The Last Supper (Maundy Thursday)
Ugolino di Nerio, Italian (Sienese), active 1317–1330s
Tempera and gold on panel
Robert Lehman Collection, 1975   1975.1.7

APRIL

3
Irene, martyr of Constantinople (d. 304)

4
Isidore, archbishop of Seville (ca. 560–636), Doctor of the Church

5
Vincent Ferrer (1350–1419), patron of brickmakers, patron of builders

6
Celestine, pope (d. 432)

7
Jean Baptiste de Lasalle (1651–1719), founder of the Brothers of the Christian Schools, patron of teachers of boys

8
Walter, abbot of Pontoise (ca. 1030–1099)

9
Mary of Cleophas, witness at the Crucifixion

The Three Marys and the Angel at Christ's Tomb and
Christ Meeting the Three Marys in an Initial A (Easter Sunday)
Nerius, Italian (Bolognese)
Tempera on parchment, ca. 1320
Rogers Fund, 1912   12.56.1

APRIL

10

Fulbert, bishop of Chartres (ca. 960–1028)

11

Leo the Great, pope (d. 461)

12

Zeno, bishop of Verona (d. 372), invoked against floods, invoked to help children learn to walk and talk

13

Hermenegild (d. 586), Visigothic prince martyred by his father

14

Justin, second-century martyr, patron of philosophers

15

Basilissa and Anastasia, martyrs under emperor Nero (54–68)

16

Bernadette of Lourdes (1844–1879), visionary, patron of shepherds

Saint George Killing the Dragon (April 23)
From the *Belles Heures of Jean, duke of Berry*, fol. 167r
The Limbourg Brothers, France (Paris), active ca. 1400–1416
Tempera and gold on vellum
The Cloisters Collection, 1954   54.1.1

APRIL

17

Stephen Harding, abbot of Citeaux (d. 1134)

18

Galdinus, bishop of Milan (1100–1176)

19

Leo IX, pope (1002–1054)

20

Marcian, monk of Auxerre (d. 488)

21

Anselm, archbishop of Canterbury (1033–1109)

22

Theodore of Sykeon, bishop of Anastasiopolis (d. 613),
helper of childless couples

23

George (d. ca. 303), patron of England

The Miraculous Communion of Saint Catherine of Siena (April 30)
Giovanni di Paolo, Italian (Sienese), born ca. 1400, d. 1482
Tempera and gold on panel
The Friedsam Collection, Bequest of Michael Friedsam, 1931   32.100.95

APRIL

24

Egbert, monk of Lindisfarne (d. 729)

25

Mark the Evangelist

26

Anacletus (Cletus) (r. 76–88) and Marcellinus (r. 296–304),
popes and martyrs

27

Zita of Lucca (1218–1278), patron of servants

28

Vitalis of Ravenna, third-century martyr

29

Peter Martyr (1205–1252), first martyr of the Dominican order

30

Catherine of Siena (1333?–1380), Dominican nun,
Doctor of the Church, patron of Siena and Italy

Saint Joseph (May 1)
Detail from the right wing of *Triptych of the Annunciation*
Robert Campin, Netherlandish (Bruges), ca. 1378–1444
Oil on panel
The Cloisters Collection, 1956   56.70

MAY

1	Joseph the Workman, husband of the Virgin Mary, patron of carpenters
2	Athanasius, bishop of Alexandria (ca. 296–373), Doctor of the Church
3	The Finding of the Holy Cross
4	Monica (332–387), mother of Saint Augustine of Hippo, patron of wives
5	Pius V, pope (1504–1572)
6	John the Evangelist before the Latin Gate
7	Stanislaus, bishop of Cracow (ca. 1030–1079), patron of Poland

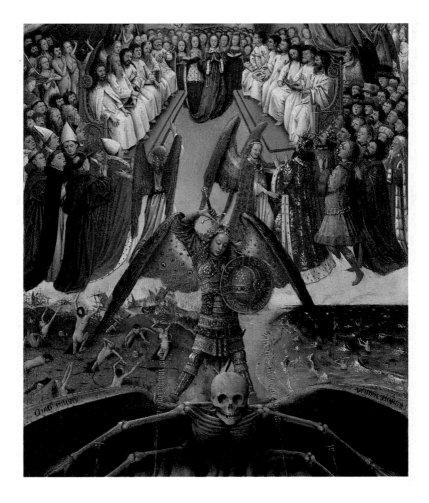

The Archangel Michael (May 8)
Detail from *The Last Judgment*
Jan van Eyck, Netherlandish, active by 1422, d. 1441
Oil on canvas, transferred from panel
Fletcher Fund, 1933   33.92b

MAY

8

The Apparition of Saint Michael the Archangel

9

Gregory Nazianzen (329–389), Cappadocian father

10

Antoninus, archbishop of Florence (1389–1459)

11

Philip and James the Less, Apostles

12

Pancras (d. 304), patron of children

13

Robert Bellarmine, cardinal (1542–1621), prefect of the Vatican Library

14

Gerard of Villamagna (ca. 1174–1245), Tuscan hermit

Saint Bernardino Preaching (May 20)
Lorenzo di Pietro, called Vecchietta (?), Italian (Sienese), 1412–1480
Tempera on parchment
Robert Lehman Collection, 1975   1975.1.2474

MAY

15 Isidore the Husbandman (ca. 1080–ca. 1130), patron of Madrid, patron of farmers

16 Brendan (Brandon) the Navigator, abbot of Clonfert (ca. 486–ca. 573)

17 Paschal Baylon (1540–1592), lay Franciscan known as the Angel of the Eucharist

18 Eric, king of Sweden (r. 1150–1161), patron of Sweden

19 Peter Celestine, pope (1215–1296), founder of the Celestine order, patron of bookbinders

20 Bernardino of Siena (1380–1444), Franciscan reformer

21 Godric (ca. 1069–1170), English hermit and hymnist

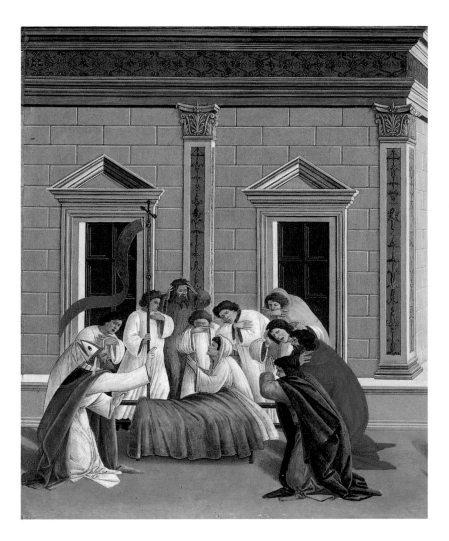

Saint Zenobius Resuscitating a Youth (May 25)
Detail from *Three Miracles of Saint Zenobius*
Sandro Botticelli, Italian (Florentine), 1445–1510
Tempera on panel
John Stewart Kennedy Fund, 1911   11.98

MAY

Julia, fifth-century martyr, patron of Corsica

22

Ivo, bishop of Chartres (ca. 1040–1116), patron of abandoned children

23

David I, king of Scotland (ca. 1085–1153)

24

Zenobius, bishop of Florence (d. ca. 390)

25

Philip Neri (1515–1595), founder of Oratorians, invoked against rheumatism

26

Bede the Venerable (ca. 673–735), father of English history

27

Augustine, first archbishop of Canterbury (d. 604/5)

28

The Coronation of the Virgin (May 31)
Niccolò di Buonaccorso, Italian (Sienese), active 1370s–1388
Tempera and gold on panel
Robert Lehman Collection, 1975   1975.1.21

MAY-JUNE

29 Mary Magdalen dei Pazzi (1566–1607), Carmelite mystic

30 Joan of Arc (1412–1431), patron of France, patron of radio

31 The Queership of the Virgin

1 Angela Merici (1474–1540), founder of the Ursuline order

2 Elmo, bishop of Formiae (d. ca. 300),
patron of sailors, invoked to relieve colicky infants

3 Kevin (d. ca. 618), founding abbot of Glendalough

4 Quirinus (d. 308), martyr, honored at Tivoli

Saint Quirinus (June 4)
Exterior wing from a polyptych, *The Life and Miracles of Saint Godeleva*
Master of the Saint Godeleva Legend, Netherlandish,
active fourth quarter of the 15th century
Oil on panel
John Stewart Kennedy Fund, 1912   12.79

JUNE

5
Boniface, martyr, archbishop of Mainz (ca. 675–754)

6
Norbert, archbishop of Magdeburg (ca. 1080–1134),
founder of the Premonstratensian order

7
Willibald, bishop of Eichstatt in Bavaria (d. 786)

8
Médard, bishop of Noyon (ca. 456–560), invoked against toothache

9
Richard, first bishop of Andria (twelfth century)

10
Margaret, queen of Scotland (ca. 1045–1093)

11
Barnabus, Apostle

Saint Anthony of Padua (June 13)
Maso di Banco, Italian (Florentine), active 1320–1346
Tempera and gold on panel
Maitland F. Griggs Collection
Bequest of Maitland F. Griggs, 1943   43.98.13

JUNE

Onuphrius, fourth-century hermit, patron of weavers

12

Anthony of Padua (1195–1231), invoked for help in finding lost possessions

13

Basil the Great, bishop of Caesarea (ca. 330–379), Doctor of the Church

14

Vitus (Guy) (d. 404), patron of dancers

15

Benno, bishop of Meissen (1010–1106),
patron of fishermen, invoked for rain

16

Harvey, monk of Brittany (d. 568),
invoked to quiet frogs, invoked against eye trouble

17

Mark and Marcellian (d. ca. 290), twin Roman martyrs

18

Scenes from the Life of Saint John the Baptist (June 24)
Master of James IV of Scotland, Netherlandish (Bruges)
Tempera and gold on parchment, ca. 1515
Bequest of George D. Pratt, 1935   48.149.16

JUNE

Gervase and Protase, first martyrs of Milan

19

Silverius, pope (r. 536–537)

20

Ralph (Raoul), ninth-century archbishop of Bourges

21

Thomas More (1478–1535), patron of lawyers

22

Audrey (Ethelreda), Queen of East Anglia (d. 679),
founder and abbess of Ely

23

The Birth of Saint John the Baptist

24

William of Vercelli (1085–1142), hermit monk,
advisor to King Robert I of Naples

25

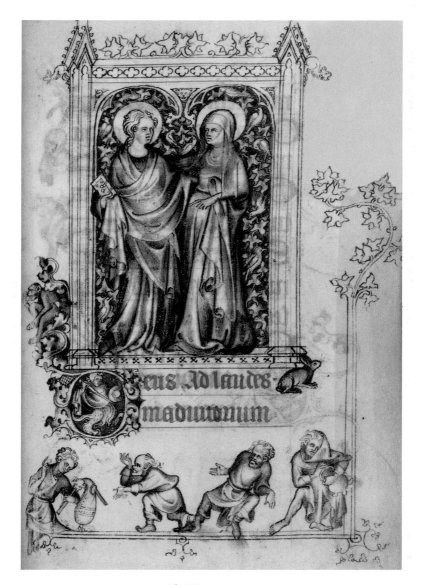

The Visitation (July 2)
From *The Hours of Jeanne d'Evreux*, fol. 35
Jean Pucelle, French (Paris), active ca. 1320–1350
Tempera and gold on parchment
The Cloisters Collection, 1954   54.1.2

JUNE-JULY

John and Paul (d. ca. 362), Roman martyrs

26

Ladislaus (Laszlo), king of Hungary (1040–1095)

27

Irenaeus (ca. 125–202), patron of Lyons

28

Peter and Paul, Apostles

29

Commemoration of Saint Paul, Apostle of the Gentiles

30

Thierry (Theodoric) of Reims, abbot of Mont d'Or (d. 533)

1

The Visitation

2

The Life and Miracles of Saint Godeleva (July 6)
Central panel of a polyptych
Master of the Saint Godeleva Legend, Netherlandish, active fourth quarter of the 15th century
Oil on panel
John Stewart Kennedy Fund, 1912   12.79

JULY

3   Julius and Aaron (d. ca. 304), martyrs of Wales

4   Bertha (d. ca. 725), founder of the convent of Blangy-en-Artois

5   Athanasius the Athonite (ca. 920–1003),
founder of the Lavra monastery on Mount Athos

6   Godeleva (ca. 1049–1070), persecuted by her mother-in-law,
patron of Bruges

7   Felix, bishop of Nantes (ca. 513–582)

8   Elizabeth, queen of Portugal (1271–1337)

9   Veronica Giuliani (1660–1727), abbess and mystic

The Crucifix Acknowledging the Prayers of Saint John Gualbert (July 12)
Attributed to Niccolò di Pietro Gerini, Italian (Florentine), active by 1368, d. 1414/15
Tempera and gold on panel
Gwynne Andrews Fund, 1958   58.135

JULY

10	Seven brothers, second-century Roman martyrs
11	Olga (ca. 879–969), Russian princess
12	John Gualbert (985–1073), founder of the Vallombrosan order
13	Mildred (d. ca. 700), English abbess
14	Bonaventure (1221–1274), Franciscan scholar known as the "Seraphic Doctor"
15	Henry II, Holy Roman Emperor (973–1024)
16	Fulrad, abbot of Saint-Denis (d. 777)

Saint Margaret Emerging from the Dragon (July 20)
From the *Belles Heures of Jean, duke of Berry*, fol. 177r
The Limbourg Brothers, France (Paris), active ca. 1400–1416
Tempera and gold on vellum
The Cloisters Collection, 1954   54.1.1

JULY

17	Alexis of Rome (fifth century?), became a pilgrim on his wedding night
18	Arnulf, bishop of Metz (d. 643)
19	Vincent de Paul (1581–1660), patron of charitable societies
20	Margaret of Antioch, patron of childbirth
21	Praxedes, first- or second-century virgin of Rome
22	Mary Magdalene, patron of repentant sinners
23	Apollinaris, first bishop of Ravenna (d. ca. 200)

Saint James the Greater (July 25)
Netherlandish or North German, ca. 1500
Tempera and gold on parchment
The Friedsam Collection
Bequest of Michael Friedsam, 1932   32.100.475d

JULY

24   Christina, fourth-century (?) virgin and martyr

25   James the Greater, Apostle, patron of laborers, patron of pilgrims

26   Anne and Joachim, parents of the Virgin Mary;
Anne is patron of housewives

27   Pantaleon (d. ca. 305), patron of midwives

28   Victor I, pope (d. 198)

29   Martha, sister of Lazarus, patron of housewives

30   Julitta, fourth-century widow and martyr

Saint Dominic Resuscitating Napoleone Orsini (August 4)
Bartolomeo degli Erri, Italian (Modenese), active 1460–1479
Tempera on canvas, transferred from panel
The Bequest of Michael Dreicer, 1921   22.60.59

JULY-AUGUST

Ignatius of Loyola (1491–1556), founder of the Jesuit order

31

Saint Peter in Chains

1

Thomas of Dover (d. 1295), Benedictine monk

2

Finding of the Body of Saint Stephen, first martyr

3

Dominic (ca. 1170–1221), founder of the Dominican order

4

Our Lady of the Snows (founding of Santa Maria Maggiore in Rome)

5

The Transfiguration of Christ

6

Saint Laurence in an Initial C (August 10)
Don Simone, Italian (Florentine), active ca. 1380–ca. 1410
Tempera and gold on parchment
Bequest of Mrs. A. M. Minturn, 1890   90.61.2

AUGUST

7

Donatus, bishop of Arezzo (d. 362)

8

Altmann of Passau (d. 1091), chaplain of Holy Roman Emperor Henry III

9

Oswald, martyred king of Northumbria (d. 642)

10

Laurence, deacon martyr (d. 258), patron of chefs

11

Alexander the Charcoal-burner, third-century bishop of Comana

12

Clare (1194–1253), founder of the second order of
Saint Francis (Poor Clares), patron of television

13

Hippolytus and Cassian, third-century Roman martyrs

The Assumption of the Virgin in an Initial V (August 15)
Nicola di ser Sozzo, Italian (Sienese), active 1348–1363
Tempera and gold on parchment
Gift of Louis L. Lorillard, 1896   96.32.12

AUGUST

14

Eusebius of Rome, fourth-century martyr

15

The Assumption of the Virgin

16

Roch (ca. 1350–ca. 1380), hermit, invoked against plague and cholera

17

Hyacinth (1185–1257), Dominican missionary to Poland and Russia,
invoked against drowning

18

Helena, empress (ca. 250–329),
mother of Constantine and finder of the True Cross

19

Louis of Anjou, bishop of Toulouse (1274–1297),
patron of the third order of Saint Francis

20

Bernard, abbot of Clairvaux (ca. 1090–1153), patron of candlemakers

Procession with the Relics of Saint Louis (August 25)
From *The Hours of Jeanne d'Evreux*, fol. 173v
Jean Pucelle, French (Paris), active ca. 1320–1350
Tempera and gold on parchment
The Cloisters Collection, 1954   54.1.2

AUGUST

Joan Frances de Chantal (1572–1641), founder of the order of the Visitation

21

Sigfrid, abbot of Wearmouth (d. 688)

22

Rose of Lima (d. 1617), first canonized saint of the New World,
patron of South America

23

Bartholomew, Apostle, patron of tanners, patron of plasterers

24

Louis IX, king of France (1214–1270)

25

Yrieix, abbot of Attane (d. ca. 591)

26

Caesarius, bishop of Arles (ca. 470–542)

27

The Investiture of Saint Augustine (August 28)
Detail from the central panel of an altarpiece,
Scenes from the Life of Saint Augustine
Master of Saint Augustine, Netherlandish, active ca. 1490–1500
Oil and silver on panel
The Cloisters Collection, 1961   61.199

AUGUST-SEPTEMBER

28
Augustine, bishop of Hippo (354–430), Doctor of the Church.

29
The Beheading of Saint John the Baptist

30
Fiacre of Brie (d. 670), patron of gardeners

31
Aidan (d. 651), founder of the monastery of Lindisfarne

1
Giles (d. ca. 710), patron of blacksmiths,
patron of the physically disabled, patron of nursing mothers

2
Stephen, king of Hungary (ca. 975–1038)

3
Pius X, pope (1835–1914)

The Birth of the Virgin in an Initial G (September 8)
Don Silvestro dei Gherarducci, Italian (Florentine), 1339–1399
Tempera and gold on parchment
Rogers Fund, 1921   21.168

SEPTEMBER

4
Ida (d. 820), founder of the church of Herzfeld

5
Bertin, abbot of Saint-Bertin (d. 698)

6
Bee, seventh-century Irish nun

7
Regina, second-century martyr of Autun

8
The Birth of the Virgin

9
Kieran, abbot of Clonmacnoise (ca. 512–ca. 545)

10
Nicholas of Tolentino (1245–1306), Augustinian friar
who converted notorious sinners, patron of infants

The Exaltation of the Cross (September 14)
From the *Belles Heures of Jean, duke of Berry*, fol. 157r
The Limbourg Brothers, France (Paris), active ca. 1400–1416
Tempera and gold on vellum
The Cloisters Collection, 1954   54.1.1

SEPTEMBER

11

Protus and Hyacinth, third-century Roman martyrs

12

Guy of Anderlecht (d. 1012), patron of peasants,
patron of horned beasts and workhorses

13

Maurilius, bishop of Angers (d. 453)

14

The Exaltation of the Holy Cross

15

Catherine of Genoa (1447–1510), mystic and author

16

Cornelius, pope and martyr (d. 253)

17

The Stigmatization of Saint Francis

Saint Matthew (September 21)
Detail from *Saints John the Baptist and Matthew*
Bicci di Lorenzo, Italian (Florentine), 1373–1452
Tempera and gold on panel
Robert Lehman Collection, 1975   1975.1.68

SEPTEMBER

18

Joseph of Copertino (1606–1663), Franciscan,
patron of air travelers and pilots

19

Januarius (Gennaro), bishop of Benevento (d. ca. 305), patron of blood banks,
patron of Naples, invoked for protection from volcanoes

20

Eustace, martyr, patron of hunters

21

Matthew, Apostle, patron of tax collectors and customs officers

22

Thomas of Villanova, archbishop of Valencia (1486–1555)

23

Linus, pope (d. ca. 80)

24

Germer, abbot of Beauvais (d. ca. 658), invoked against fever

The Last Communion of Saint Jerome (September 30)
Sandro Botticelli, Italian (Florentine), 1445–1510
Tempera on panel
Bequest of Benjamin Altman, 1913   14.40.642

SEPTEMBER-OCTOBER

25

Finbar (Barry), bishop of Cork (ca. 560–ca. 610)

26

René Goupil (d. 1642), Canadian Jesuit,
first North-American martyr, patron of anaesthetists

27

Cosmas and Damian (d. 303), martyrs,
patrons of barbers, patrons of doctors

28

Wenceslaus (Vaclav), duke of Bohemia (907–929),
patron of Bohemia, the Czech Republic, and Moravia; patron of brewers

29

Dedication of Saint Michael Archangel, Rome

30

Jerome (ca. 341–420), Doctor of the Church, translator of the Bible into Latin,
patron of librarians and students

1

Remigius (Remi), bishop of Reims (d. 533)

Saint Francis Receiving the Stigmata (October 4)
Right wing of a triptych
Gerard David, Netherlandish, active by 1484, d. 1523
Oil on panel
The Friedsam Collection
Bequest of Michael Friedsam, 1931   32.100.40c

OCTOBER

The Guardian Angels

2

Theresa of Lisieux (1873–1897), patron of aviators,
patron of missions, patron of France

3

Francis of Assisi (1186–1226), founder of the Franciscan order,
patron of ecologists

4

Flora of Beaulieu (1309–1347), visionary

5

Bruno (ca. 1032–1101), founder of the Carthusian order

6

Sergius and Bacchus, fourth-century martyrs

7

Bridget of Sweden (1303–1373), founder of the Bridgettine order,
patron of Sweden

8

Saint Bruno Entering the Grande Chartreuse (October 6)
From the *Belles Heures of Jean, duke of Berry*, fol. 97r
The Limbourg Brothers, France (Paris), active ca. 1400–1416
Tempera and gold on vellum
The Cloisters Collection, 1954   54.1.1

OCTOBER

9	Denis, bishop of Paris (d. ca. 250), patron of France
10	Francis Borgia, General of the Jesuits (1510–1572), began missionary work in the Americas
11	Kenneth (ca. 525–ca. 600), Irish abbot, cautioned birds not to sing on Sunday
12	Edwin, king of Northumbria (584–633)
13	Edward the Confessor, king of England (1033–1066)
14	Calixtus, pope (d. 222)
15	Teresa of Ávila (1515–1582), Carmelite reformer and mystic, first woman to be named Doctor of the Church

Saint Ursula and the Martyrdom of the Eleven Thousand Virgins (October 21)
From the *Belles Heures of Jean, duke of Berry,* fol. 178v
The Limbourg Brothers, France (Paris), active ca. 1400–1416
Tempera and gold on vellum
The Cloisters Collection, 1954   54.1.1

OCTOBER

16

Hedwig, Duchess of Silesia (ca. 1175–1243), patron of Silesia

17

Margaret Mary Alacoque (1647–1690), Saint of the Sacred Heart

18

Luke the Evangelist, painter of the Virgin, patron of painters

19

Peter of Alcantara (1499–1562), Franciscan priest

20

Acca, bishop of Hexham (d. 740)

21

Ursula, fourth-century (?) virgin martyr

22

Donatus the Scot, bishop of Fiesole (d. 874/7)

The Archangel Raphael and Tobias (October 24)
Neri di Bicci, Italian (Florentine), 1419–1491
Tempera on panel
Robert Lehman Collection, 1975   1975.1.71

OCTOBER

23 Severinus, fourth-century bishop of Cologne

24 The Archangel Raphael, patron of the blind

25 Crispin and Crispinian (d. ca. 285), Roman martyrs, patrons of cobblers

26 Bean, first bishop of Morthlach in Banff (eleventh century)

27 Odran, monk of Iona (d. ca. 563)

28 Simon and Jude, Apostles

29 Colman (d. ca. 632), Irish bishop

The Virgin Surrounded by Saints in an Initial E (November 1)
The Osservanza Master, Italian (Sienese), second quarter of the 14th century
Tempera on parchment
Robert Lehman Collection, 1975   1975.1.2484

OCTOBER-NOVEMBER

Marcellus the Centurion, martyr (d. 298)

30

Wolfgang, bishop of Regensburg (924–994)

31

All Saints

1

All Souls

2

Winifrid (d. ca. 650), Welsh virgin

3

Charles Borromeo, archbishop of Milan (1538–1584), patron of seminarians

4

Elizabeth and Zachary, parents of Saint John the Baptist

5

Saint Martin Giving Half His Cloak to a Beggar (November 11)
From the *Belles Heures of Jean, duke of Berry*, fol. 169r
The Limbourg Brothers, France (Paris), active ca. 1400–1416
Tempera and gold on vellum
The Cloisters Collection, 1954   54.1.1

NOVEMBER

6
Leonard, abbot of Noblat (d. ca. 560), protector of prisoners

7
Engelbert, archbishop of Cologne (1185–1225)

8
The Four Crowned Martyrs (Claudius, Nicostratus, Simpronian, Castorius), early fourth-century Romans, patrons of stonemasons

9
Dedication of Saint John Lateran, Rome

10
Andrew Avellino (1521–1608), invoked against unexpected death

11
Martin, bishop of Tours (ca. 316–397), patron of the impoverished

12
Cadwaladr, king of Wales (d. 664)

Sermon of Saint Albert the Great (November 15)
Friedrich Walther, German, born ca. 1440, d. 1494
Oil on panel
The Cloisters Collection, 1964   64.215

NOVEMBER

Stanislaus Kostka (1550–1568), Polish Jesuit, patron of young students

13

Laurence O'Toole, archbishop of Dublin (1128–1180)

14

Albert the Great, bishop of Regensburg (1206–1280), patron of scientists

15

Gertrude the Great (d. 1302), Benedictine nun and mystic

16

Gregory, bishop of Tours (539–594)

17

Odo, abbot of Cluny (897–942)

18

Elizabeth, queen of Hungary (1207–1231),
patron of the third order of Saint Francis

19

Saint Catherine of Alexandria in Her Study (November 25)
From the *Belles Heures of Jean, duke of Berry*, fol. 15r
The Limbourg Brothers, France (Paris), active ca. 1400–1416
Tempera and gold on vellum
The Cloisters Collection, 1954   54.1.1

NOVEMBER

20	Edmund, king of the English (ca. 840–869)
21	The Presentation of the Virgin
22	Cecilia, third-century Roman martyr, patron of musicians
23	Clement, pope and martyr (d. ca. 100), patron of stonecutters
24	John of the Cross (1542–1591), Spanish Carmelite mystic
25	Catherine of Alexandria, fourth-century martyr, patron of students
26	Conrad, bishop of Constance (ca. 900–975)

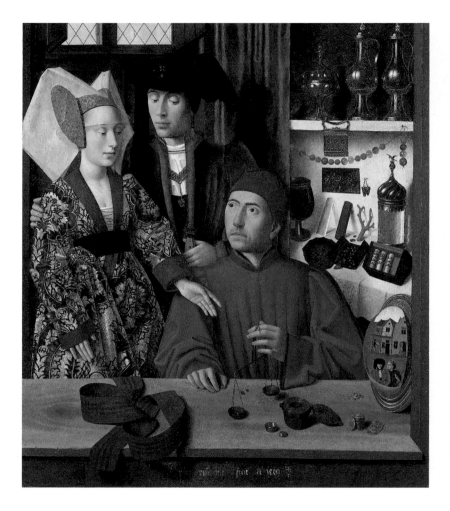

Saint Eligius (December 1)
Petrus Christus, Netherlandish, active by 1444, d. 1475/76
Oil on oak
Robert Lehman Collection, 1975   1975.1.110

Fergus, eighth-century Irish bishop

27

Stephen the Younger (d. 767), martyr for the use of icons

28

Saturninus, first bishop of Toulouse (d. 250)

29

Andrew, Apostle, patron of Scotland

30

Eligius, bishop of Noyon (ca. 590–659),
patron of goldsmiths, patron of veterinarians

1

Bibiana (Viviana) of Rome (d. 363), invoked against drunkenness

2

Francis Xavier (1506–1551), Jesuit missionary, patron of foreign missions

3

Saint Nicholas Saving Seafarers (December 6)
From the *Belles Heures of Jean, duke of Berry*, fol. 168r
The Limbourg Brothers, France (Paris), active ca. 1400–1416
Tempera and gold on vellum
The Cloisters Collection, 1954   54.1.1

DECEMBER

4	Barbara, patron of stonemasons, invoked for protection from lightning
5	Crispina of Tagora, martyr (d. 304)
6	Nicholas, fourth-century bishop of Myra, patron of children
7	Ambrose, bishop of Milan (339–397), Doctor of the Church
8	The Immaculate Conception
9	Valerie, third-century martyr of Limoges
10	Eulalia of Merida, virgin martyr (d. ca. 304)

Saint Lucy Resisting Efforts to Move Her (December 13)
Giovanni di Bartolommeo Cristiani, Italian (Florentine), active 1367–1398
Tempera and gold on panel
Rogers Fund, 1912   12.41.2

DECEMBER

Damasus, pope (ca. 304–384)

11

Finnian, abbot of Clonard (d. 549), Teacher of Irish Saints

12

Lucy, virgin martyr (d. 304), invoked against eye diseases

13

Venantius Fortunatus, bishop of Poitiers (ca. 530–ca. 610), hymnist

14

Nino, fourth-century virgin, apostle to Georgia

15

Adelaide (931–999), mother of Holy Roman Emperor Otto II

16

Lazarus, whom Jesus raised from the dead

17

Saint Thomas (December 21)
Detail from *Saints Matthias and Thomas*
Bartolomeo Bulgarini (Ugolino Lorenzetti), Italian (Sienese), active 1337–1378
Tempera and gold on panel
Robert Lehman Collection, 1975   1975.1.8

DECEMBER

Flannan, seventh-century Irish bishop

18

Anastasius I, pope (r. 399–410)

19

Dominic, abbot of Silos (ca. 1000–1073)

20

Thomas, Apostle, patron of architects and builders

21

Frances Xavier Cabrini (1850–1917), founder of the Missionary Sisters of the Sacred Heart, first United States citizen to be canonized

22

Anatolia, Audace, and Victoria (d. ca. 250) Roman martyrs

23

Tharsilla, virgin martyr of Rome (d. ca. 550)

24

The Nativity (December 25)
Francesco Marmitta, Italian (Emilian), 1457–1505
Tempera on parchment
Robert Lehman Collection, 1975   1975.1.2491

DECEMBER

The Nativity

25

Saint John on Patmos (December 27)
From *The Cloisters Apocalypse*, fol. 3r
France, Normandy (Manche), Coutances, 1300–1325
Tempera, gold, silver, and ink on vellum
The Cloisters Collection, 1968   68.174

DECEMBER

26

Stephen (d. ca. 35), first Christian martyr, patron of bricklayers

27

John the Evangelist

28

Holy Innocents, the infants of Bethlehem murdered at the order of King Herod

29

Thomas Becket, archbishop of Canterbury (1118–1170)

30

Egwin, bishop of Worcester (d. 717)

31

Silvester I, pope (d. 335)

Index

Capital letters indicate saints, feast days, and events illustrated in the book.

Bonifice, June 5

Brendan (Brandon) the Navigator, May 16

Bridget of Sweden, October 8

Brigid of Ireland, February 1

BRUNO, October 6

Cadwaladr, king of Wales, November 12

Caesarius, August 27

Calixtus, October 14

Canute, January 19

Casimir, March 4

Cassian (with Hippolytus), August 13

Catherine dei Ricci, February 13

CATHERINE OF ALEXANDRIA, November 25

Catherine of Genoa, September 15

CATHERINE OF SIENA, April 30

Cecilia, November 22

Celestine, April 6

Chad, March 2

CHARLEMAGNE, January 28

Charles Borromeo, November 4

Christina, July 24

CIRCUMCISION OF CHRIST, January 1

Clare, August 12

Clement, November 23

Colman, October 29

Commemoration of Saint Paul, June 30

Conrad of Constance, November 26

Conrad of Piacenza, February 19

Conversion of Saint Paul of Tarsus, January 25

Cornelius, September 16

Cosmas and Damian, September 27

Crispin and Crispinian, October 25

Crispina of Tagora, December 5

Cunegund, March 3

Cuthbert, March 20

Cyril, March 29

Damasus, December 11

Damian (with Cosmas), September 27

David, March 1

David I, king of Scotland, May 24

Dedication of Saint John Lateran,
    November 9

Dedication of Saint Michael Archangel,
    September 29

Denis, October 9

Deogratias, March 22

DOMINIC, August 4

Dominic, abbot of Silos, December 20

Donatus, August 7

Donatus the Scot, October 22

DOROTHY, February 6

Edmund, king of the English, November 20

Edward the Confessor, king of England, October 13

Edward the Martyr, March 18

Edwin, king of Northumbria, October 12

Egbert, April 24

Egwin, December 30

Eleutherius, February 20

ELIGIUS, December 1

Elizabeth, queen of Hungary, November 19

Elizabeth, queen of Portugal, July 8

Elizabeth and Zachary, November 5

Elizabeth Seton, January 4

Elmo, June 2

Engelbert, November 7

EPIPHANY, January 6

Eric, May 18

Eulalia, December 10

Eusebius, August 14

Eustace, September 20

Rose of Lima, August 23

Saint John Lateran, Dedication of, November 9

Saint Michael Archangel, Dedication of,
    September 29

Saturninus, November 29

Scholastica, February 10

Sebastian, January 20

Sergius and Bacchus, October 7

Seven brothers, July 10

Severinus, October 23

Sigfrid, February 15

Sigfrid, abbot of Wearmouth, August 22

Silverius, June 20

Silvester I, December 31

Simeon, February 18

Simeon Stylites, January 5

Simon and Jude, October 28

Sophronius, March 11

Stanislaus Kostka, November 13

Stanislaus of Cracow, May 7

Stephen, December 26

Stephen, Finding of the Body of, August 3

Stephen Harding, April 17

Stephen of Hungary, September 2

Stephen of Muret, February 8

Stephen the Younger, November 28

Stigmatization of Saint Francis, September 17

Teresa of Ávila, October 15

Tharsilla, December 24

Theodore of Sykeon, April 22

THEODULUS, February 17

Theresa of Lisieux, October 3

Thierry of Reims, July 1

THOMAS, December 21

THOMAS AQUINAS, March 7

Thomas Becket, December 29

Thomas More, June 22

Thomas of Dover, August 2

Thomas of Villanova, September 22

Tillo, January 7

Timothy, January 24

Transfiguration of Christ, August 6

Turibius, March 23

URSULA, October 21

Valentine, February 14

Valerie, December 9

Venantius Fortunatus, December 14

Veronica Giuliani, July 9

Victor I, July 28

Victoria (with Anatolia and Audace), December 23

Victorinus, February 25

Vincent de Paul, July 19

Vincent Ferrer, April 5

Vincent of Saragossa, January 22

VISITATION, July 2

Vitalis of Ravenna, April 28

Vitus (Guy), June 15

Walter, April 8

Wenceslaus (Vaclav), September 28

Willibald, June 7

William, January 10

William of Vercelli, June 25

Winifrid, November 3

Wolfgang, October 31

Yrieix, August 26

Zachary, March 15

Zachary (with Elizabeth), November 5

Zeno, April 12

ZENOBIUS, May 25

Zita of Lucca, April 27

Cover:
Saint George Killing the Dragon
From the *Belles Heures of Jean, duke of Berry*, fol. 167r
The Limbourg Brothers, France (Paris), active 1400–1416
Tempera and gold on vellum
The Cloisters Collection, 1954   54.1.1

Frontispiece:
Saint Francis and the Bishop of Assisi Admit Saint Clare to the Franciscan Order
German (Nuremberg), 1360–70
Tempera and gold on panel
The Cloisters Collection, 1984   1984.343

Title page border and calendar border adapted from the *Belles Heures of Jean, duke of Berry*; calendar border adaptation by Barry Girsh.

Photography: opposite week of March 20, Malcolm Varon, New York; opposite week of April 24, Geoffrey Clements; all other photography by The Metropolitan Museum of Art Photograph Studio.